How to use this book

Follow the advice, in italics, given for teachers on each page.
Support the children as they read the text that is shaded in cream.
Praise *the children at every step!*

Detailed guidance is provided in the Read Write Inc. Phonics Handbook

8 reading activities

Children:
- *Practise reading the speed sounds.*
- *Read the green and red words for the story.*
- *Listen as you read the introduction.*
- *Discuss the vocabulary check with you.*
- *Read the story.*
- *Re-read the story and discuss the 'questions to talk about'.*
- *Re-read the story with fluency and expression.*
- *Practise reading the speed words.*

D0476690

Speed sounds

Consonants *Say the pure sounds (do not add 'uh').*

f	l ll	m	n	r	s ss	v	z (s)	(sh)	(th)	ng nk

b	c k ck	d	g	h	j	p	qu	t (tt)	w	x	y	(ch)

Vowels *Say the sounds in and out of order.*

at	hen	in	on	up	day	see	high	blow	zoo

*Each box contains one sound but sometimes more than one grapheme. Focus graphemes are **circled**.*

Green words

hat   wi<u>th</u>   stop   <u>ch</u>ip   bag   bun   big   bed   <u>th</u>is

<u>sh</u>op   →   <u>sh</u>ops   grab   →   grabs

spot   →   spo<u>tt</u>y

Red words

<u>th</u>e   of   he   Baby

5

Vocabulary check

Discuss the meaning (as used in the story) after the children have read the word.

definition:

grab   *snatch*

Punctuation to note in this story:

Big Blob, Baby Blob	*Capital letters for names*
He **This** **Stop** **In**	*Capital letters that start sentences*
.	*Full stop at the end of each sentence*
!	*Exclamation mark used to show anger*
...	*Wait and see*

Big Blob and Baby Blob

Introduction

You probably know of a toddler who does not know how to behave when he/she goes shopping. What sort of things does he/she get up to?

Baby Blob and Big Blob are monsters. They go shopping together, but Baby Blob does not realise that he cannot help himself to anything he wants.

Story written by Gill Munton
Illustrated by Tim Archbold

This is Big Blob
with Baby Blob.

Big Blob is at the shops
with Baby Blob.

In the hat shop ...

Baby Blob grabs a red spotty hat.
He puts it on.

Ga ga ga

"Stop it, Baby Blob!"

In the chip shop ...

Baby Blob grabs a bag of chips.

Ga ga ga

"Stop it, Baby Blob!"

In the bun shop ...

Baby Blob grabs a big bun.

Ga ga ga

"Stop it, Baby Blob!"

In the bed shop ...

Zzz zzz zzz

Questions to talk about

FIND IT QUESTIONS

✓ *Turn to the page*

✓ *Read the question to the children*

✓ *Find the answer*

Page 10: *What does Baby Blob grab in the hat shop?*
What does Big Blob say?

Page 11: *What does Baby Blob grab in the chip shop?*
What does Big Blob say?

Page 12: *What does Baby Blob grab in the bun shop?*
What does Big Blob say?

Page 13: *What happens in the bed shop?*